BASIC PNEUMATICS

3

LEARNING ACTIVITY PACKET

PRINCIPLES OF PNEUMATIC PRESSURE AND FLOW

AMATROL®

BB834-BA03XEN

PRINCIPLES OF PNEUMATIC PRESSURE AND FLOW

INTRODUCTION

Previous LAPs discussed the construction and operation of basic pneumatic circuits and how they are shown using standard symbols. Before going further, it is important to understand the principles that allow power to be transmitted by a pressurized gas. With a good understanding, skills can then be developed that are used in analyzing, specifying, and troubleshooting pneumatic components.

This LAP and the next one will provide you with the basic foundation principles of pneumatics.

ITEMS NEEDED

Amatrol Supplied
    1   85-BP Basic Pneumatics Learning System

School Supplied
    1   Compressed Air Supply
    2   Rulers

SECOND EDITION, LAP 3, REV. A

Amatrol, AMNET, CIMSOFT, MCL, MINI-CIM, IST, ITC, VEST, and Technovate are trademarks or registered trademarks of Amatrol, Inc. All other brand and product names are trademarks or registered trademarks of their respective companies.

Copyright © 2011 by AMATROL, INC.

Amatrol,Inc., 2400 Centennial Blvd., Jeffersonville, IN 47130 USA, Ph 812-288-8285, FAX 812-283-1584 www.amatrol.com

TABLE OF CONTENTS

SEGMENT 1

PRESSURE VS. CYLINDER FORCE

OBJECTIVE 1	DESCRIBE HOW TO CALCULATE THE FORCE OUTPUT OF AN EXTENDING CYLINDER

If a pneumatic cylinder is extending a load, as shown in figure 1, the pressure of the air is exerted over all the surfaces in the cap end of the cylinder. However, only on the area of the piston does this pressure exert a force to move the load. The force output of the cylinder rod therefore depends on the area of this piston and the pressure in the cap end of the cylinder.

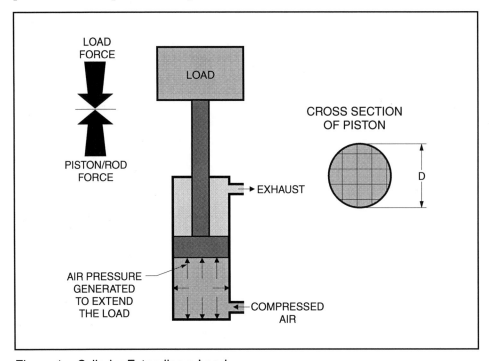

Figure 1. Cylinder Extending a Load

Since the piston is circular, the area of the piston can be obtained by using the formula for a circle: pr2 or 0.7854d2. The theoretical amount of force which is exerted by an extending cylinder can then be stated as follows:

FORMULA: FORCE OUTPUT OF CYLINDER DURING EXTENSION

$$F_p = P \times A_p$$

U.S. Customary Units:

$$F_p = P \times A_p$$
$$= P \times D^2 \times 0.7854$$

S.I. Units:

$$F_p = P \times A_p \times 0.1$$
$$= P \times D^2 \times 0.7854 \times 0.1$$

Where:

F_p = *Force output of cylinder rod extending (lbs or Newtons)*

P = *Pressure on piston (psi or kPa)*

A_p = *Area of piston (in² or cm²)*

D = *Diameter of piston (in or cm)*

NOTE

The 0.1 factor in the S.I. units occurs in converting meters and Pascals to centimeters and kPa.

Procedure Overview

In this procedure, you will calculate the theoretical force output of the cylinders used on the 850 Series pneumatic trainer for several pressures. In step 1, you will be given an example, then you will do it yourself.

❑ 1. Let's assume you have a cylinder with a bore of 2.0 in/5.08 cm and a pressure of 1000 psi/6900 kPa. The force output of the cylinder would be calculated as follows:

U.S. Customary Units:
$$F = P \times D^2 \times 0.7854$$
$$= 1000 \times (2)^2 \times 0.7854$$
$$= 1000 \times 4 \times 0.7854$$
$$= 3,142 \ lbs$$

S.I. Units:
$$F = P \times D^2 \times 0.07854$$
$$= 6900 \times (5.08)^2 \times 0.07854$$
$$= 6900 \times 25.81 \times 0.07854$$
$$= 13,987 \ N$$

❑ 2. Now calculate the theoretical force of extension of the three cylinders used in the 850 series pneumatic trainer for each of the pressures shown in the table. Use the formula for the force output of a cylinder during extension.

For the 850 Series pneumatic trainer, the piston diameter of the large bore cylinder is 1.5 in (3.81 cm), the piston diameter of the small bore cylinder is 1.125 in (2.86 cm), and the piston diameter of the single-acting cylinder is 0.75 in (1.91 cm).

PRESSURE (psi/kPa)	THEORETICAL EXTENSION FORCE		
	Large Cylinder (lbs/N)	Small Cylinder (lbs/N)	Single-Acting Cylinder (lbs/N)
10/68.9	/	/	/
15/103.5	/	/	/
20/138	/	/	/
25/172.5	/	/	/
30/207	/	/	/
40/276	/	/	/
60/414	/	/	/

❑ 3. Calculate the minimum pressure needed to support the load shown in figure 2.

Minimum Pressure Needed = _____ psi/kPa

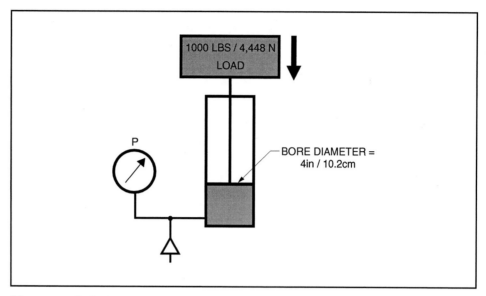

Figure 2.   Cylinder Under Load

NOTE

This is a typical application of the F = P x A formula.

Procedure Overview

In this procedure, you will measure the distance that the spring in the single-acting cylinder is compressed by the cylinder rod, when pressure is applied. From these measurements you will be able to determine the actual force output of a cylinder during extension.

❑ 1. Connect the circuit shown in figures 3 and 4.

In this circuit, compressed air will be applied to the single-acting cylinder's piston. This air pressure will create a force on the cylinder rod which will compress the spring inside the cylinder.

If we use a ruler to measure the compression of the spring, we can measure the force output of the cylinder. You'll see shortly how we do this.

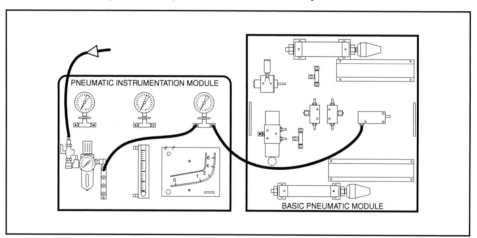

Figure 3. Pictorial of Circuit for Measuring Force Output of a Cylinder in Extension

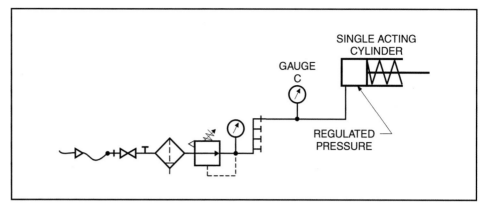

Figure 4.   Schematic of Circuit for Measuring Force Output of a Cylinder in Extension

The actual force output of a cylinder can be measured by placing a spring against a cylinder rod to resist movement, as shown in figure 5.

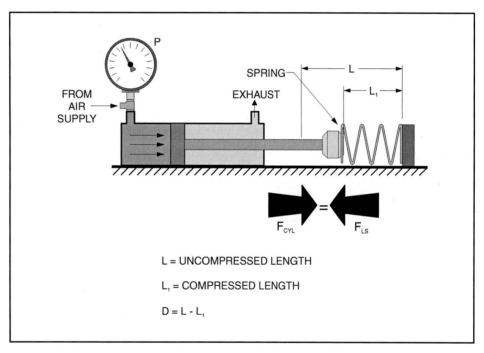

Figure 5.   Measuring Cylinder Force Output Using a Spring

The spring reacts to a load by compressing to a length where the spring force balances the load force. If the pressure increases, the spring compresses further until the forces are balanced. The force it takes to compress a spring a given distance is constant and is called the spring rate (K).

This characteristic of the spring allows us to calculate the actual force output of the cylinder by measuring the distance of spring compression and multiplying it by the spring rate. This is shown in the following formula.

FORMULA: SPRING FORCE

$$F = K \times d$$

Where

F = *Force of spring (lbs or Newtons)*
K = *Spring rate (lbs / in or Newtons / mm)*
d = *Total distance the spring is compressed (in or mm)*

The total distance compressed, d, is equal to L minus L1, as shown in figure 5.

The spring in the single-acting cylinder on the Amatrol trainer has a spring rate of about 7.1 lbs/inch (1.2 Newtons/mm). This means that a 7.1-lb force is required to compress the spring a distance of 1 inch or 1.2 Newtons to compress the spring 1 mm.

This spring, installed in the cylinder, is already compressed 0.125 in/3.175 mm. The distance must be added to any stroke measurement when determining actual force developed by the cylinder.

□ 2. Align a ruler next to the cylinder rod so that the rod end is at the 0.125 in / 3.175 mm position, as shown in figure 6.

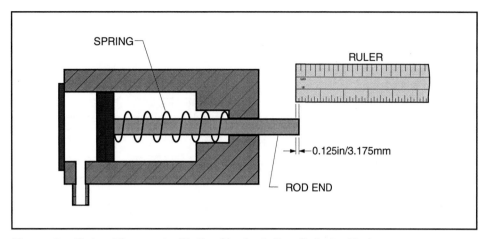

Figure 6.   Ruler Alignment with the Single-Acting Cylinder Rod

By positioning the ruler, as shown in figure 6, you will be able to read the spring compression directly from the ruler. You will not need to add 0.125 in/3.175 mm to your reading.

□ 3. Open the shut-off valve.

□ 4. Adjust the regulator pressure to 40 psi / 276 kPa and back to 0 psi / 0 kPa several times to cycle the cylinder. This is necessary to minimize friction and help lubricate the cylinder.

□ 5. Starting from 0 psi/0 kPa, slowly increase the pressure until gauge C indicates 10 psi/68.9 kPa.

You should observe that the cylinder extends partially until the spring and friction forces balance the force of the pressure across the piston.

Measure and record how far the spring is compressed for the pressure of 10 psi/68.9 kPa.

PRESSURE (psi/kPa)	DISTANCE COMPRESSED (in/mm)
10/68.9	/
15/103.5	/
20/138.0	/

□ 6. Repeat step 5 for each of the other pressures listed in the chart.

Each time you increase the pressure, you should observe that the spring compresses a little further. The more the spring is compressed, the greater its force output. The spring force is equal to the force created by the fluid pressure on the piston, which also means the cylinder's force output increases with pressure.

❑ 7. After you have completed the chart, experiment with your ability to change the position of the cylinder rod by varying the regulated pressure setting.

❑ 8. Reduce the regulator setting to minimum and close the shut-off valve.

❑ 9. Use the spring force formula and your readings from step 5 to calculate the actual force output for each pressure listed in the chart below.

PRESSURE (psi/kPa)	ACTUAL EXTENSION FORCE (lbs/N)
10/68.9	/
15/103.5	/
20/138	/

❑10. Compare these output forces with those obtained from the force formula in Skill 1.

You should find that the actual force is lower than the theoretical force you calculated. The reason for this is that the frictional force between the piston and cylinder body has been left out of the calculation.

NOTE

Designers always add at least 10% to their calculation of pressure or cylinder size theoretical to account for these frictional forces.

If the cylinder is trying to retract (pull) a load, the air pressure is exerted on all inside surfaces of the rod end of the cylinder, as shown in figure 7. As with the cap end, the only area where the pressure acts to move the load is on the piston. In this case, however, the pressure does not act on the full area of the piston because the rod is attached to it. The net area over which the pressure acts when retracting the cylinder is called the annular area or "donut area." This area is equal to the area of the piston minus the area of the rod.

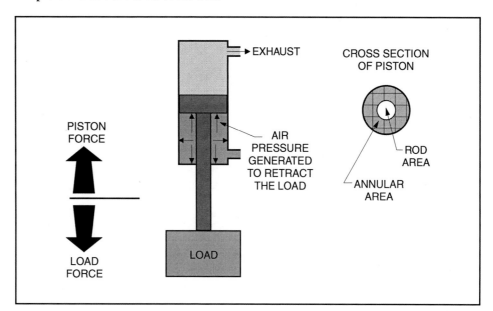

Figure 7.   Cylinder Retracting a Load

Since the donut area is less than the cap-end area, the system must generate more pressure to retract than to extend the same load. The area in the formula used to calculate the cylinder force in extension can be modified to calculate the force in retraction as follows:

FORMULA: FORCE OUTPUT OF CYLINDER RETRACTING

$$F_A = P \times A_A$$

U.S. Customary Units:

$$
\begin{aligned}
F_A &= P \times A_A \\
&= P \times [D_P{}^2 - D_R{}^2] \times 0.7854
\end{aligned}
$$

S.I. Units:

$$
\begin{aligned}
F_A &= P \times A_A \times 0.1 \\
&= P \times [D_P{}^2 - D_R{}^2] \times 0.7854 \times 0.1
\end{aligned}
$$

Where:

F_A = *Force output of cylinder rod retracting (lbs or Newtons)*

P = *Pressure on piston (psi or kPa)*

A_A = *Annular area of piston (in² or cm²)*

D_P = *Diameter of piston (in or cm)*

D_R = *Diameter of rod (in or cm)*

SKILL 3	CALCULATE THE RETRACTION FORCE OF A CYLINDER GIVEN ITS SIZE AND PRESSURE

Procedure Overview

In this procedure, you will calculate the theoretical retraction force at several different pressures for the two double-acting cylinders used in the 850 Series pneumatic trainer. In step 1, you will be given an example, then you will do it yourself.

□ 1. Let's assume you have a cylinder with a bore of 2.0 in/5.08 cm, a rod diameter of 1.0 in/2.54 cm and a pressure of 1000 psi/6900 kPa. The force output of the cylinder in retraction would be calculated as follows:

U.S. Customary Units:
$$
\begin{aligned}
F &= P \times [D_P^2 - D_R^2] \times 0.7854 \\
&= 1000 \times [2.0^2 - 1.0^2] \times 0.7854 \\
&= 1000 \times [4 - 1] \times 0.7854 \\
&= 1000 \times [3] \times 0.7854 \\
&= 2{,}356 \ lbs
\end{aligned}
$$

S.I. Units:
$$
\begin{aligned}
F &= P \times [D_P^2 - D_R^2] \times 0.07854 \\
&= 6900 \, [\, (5.08^2 - 2.54)^2] \times 0.07854 \\
&= 6900 \, [25.8 - 6.5] \times 0.07854 \\
&= 6900 \times [19.3] \times 0.07854 \\
&= 10{,}459 \ N
\end{aligned}
$$

Compare this result with the calculation of the force in extension in step 1 of skill 1. As you can see, the retraction force is less at the same pressure.

❑ 2. Now calculate the theoretical force of retraction of two cylinders for the pressures shown in the table.

For these calculations, you will be using the cylinders of the basic pneumatics module, the same as used in Skill 1. The large bore cylinder has a piston diameter of 1.5 in. (3.81 cm) and a rod diameter of 0.44 in. (1.12 cm). The small bore cylinder has a piston diameter of 1.125 in. (2.86 cm) and a rod diameter of 0.31 in. (0.79 cm).

PRESSURE (psi/kPa)	THEORETICAL RETRACTION FORCE	
	Large Cylinder (lbs/N)	Small Cylinder (lbs/N)
10/68.9	/	/
15/103.5	/	/
20/138	/	/
25/172	/	/
30/207	/	/
40/276	/	/
60/414	/	/

❑ 3. Calculate the minimum pressure needed to support the load, shown in figure 8, given the following information:

Load= 500 lbs / 2,224 Newtons
Cylinder diameter = 3 in / 7.62 cm
Rod Diameter = 1 in / 2.54 cm

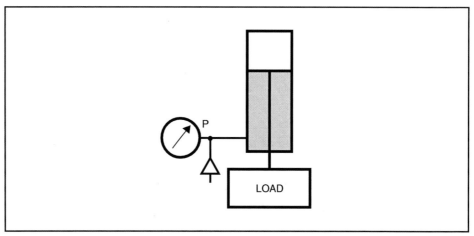

Figure 8. Cylinder Supporting a Load

Minimum pressure _____ (psi/kPa)

NOTE

This is a typical design calculation. Designers must usually calculate the load retracting as well as the load extending.

---

1. The formula for force output of cylinder during extension is Fp = _____.

2. The annular area of a cylinder is less than the cap-end (piston area) area because of the _____.

3. A(n) _____ can be used to measure the actual force output of a cylinder.

4. To compress a spring with a K value of 45 lbs/in (7.9N/mm), a total distance of 21/64ths inches (8.33 mm) would take _____ lbs/ _____ Newtons of force.

5. A 4 in/10.2 cm diameter cylinder with a 1 in/2.54 cm diameter rod will provide a theoretical push force of ___ lbs/ ____ N at 80 psi / 552 kPa.

6. The theoretical pull (retraction) force that the cylinder in question 5 would provide is _____lbs / _____ N.

7. A smaller cylinder rod in the example of question 5 would provide a(n) _____ force.

SEGMENT 2

PNEUMATIC LEVERAGE

OBJECTIVE 3	STATE PASCAL'S LAW AND EXPLAIN ITSSIGNIFICANCE IN PNEUMATICS

An earlier LAP explained that the fluid pressure at an actuator can be changed into mechanical force to perform work. The basis for this comes from a concept known as Pascal's Law. This law is named after the discoverer of this concept from the 17th Century, Blaise Pascal.

Pascal's Law states that fluid pressure in a confined vessel is transmitted undiminished to every portion of the surface of the containing vessel and acts at right angles to the surface.

The term "confined" in this application means that fluid cannot flow anywhere because it is contained on all sides by the vessel. Fluid flowing in a tube, for example, is not contained because the tube is not closed on all sides.

The concept of Pascal's Law is shown in figure 9. The weight sitting on the movable piston causes a force to be applied to a gas. Since the gas is contained by the vessel, it compresses until the pressure of the gas exerts an equal force on the piston in the opposite direction to support the weight. This same pressure exists throughout the entire volume of gas and acts perpendicular to all the surfaces of the vessel.

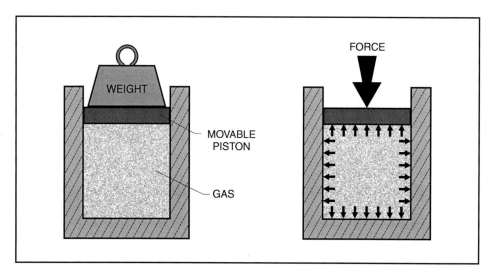

Figure 9.   Force Transmitted Through a Gas

One significance of Pascal's Law is that it makes it possible for pneumatic systems to generate a high force with a low input pressure to move a load. This concept is called pneumatic leverage. More about the details of pneumatic leverage will be discussed later in this LAP.

Another significance of Pascal's Law is a cylinder or motor will generate full force output when it first starts to move because the pressure at the actuator is high. This is a big advantage because it usually takes more force to start a load than it does once the load is moving.

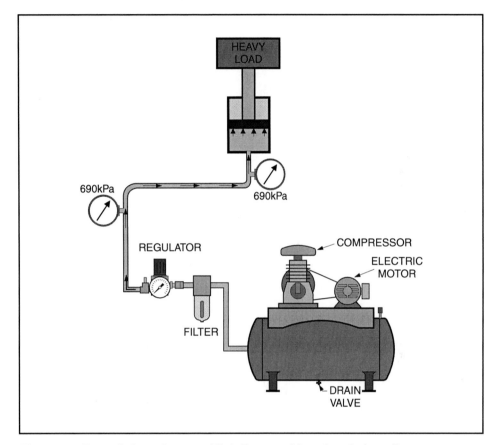

Figure 10. Pascal's Law Assures High Force to Move Loads from Rest

Electric motors can provide a high output when started too, but if the load is too great, the motor will burn up. Pneumatic systems can be stalled indefinitely without damage to the components and will produce full force at zero speed.

Activity 1. Verification of Pascal's Law

Procedure Overview

In this procedure, you will verify Pascal's Law by showing that the pressure between two points in a volume of fluid is the same if the fluid is not flowing. This will be accomplished by measuring the pressure at different points in a pneumatic system. First, you will use a simple circuit with pressure gauges and hoses, then you will demonstrate the same principle with a pneumatic cylinder.

☐ 1. Perform the following substeps to connect the air supply.

    A. Close the shutoff valve if not already closed.

    B. Adjust the regulator to its minimum setting.

    C. Connect the compressed air supply source to the supply connection located on the pneumatic instrumentation module.

☐ 2. Set up the pneumatic circuit shown in figures 11 and 12.

    This circuit has two gauges (A and B) connected at the same point in the circuit and another gauge (C) connected downstream. A directional control valve is used to stop and start the flow.

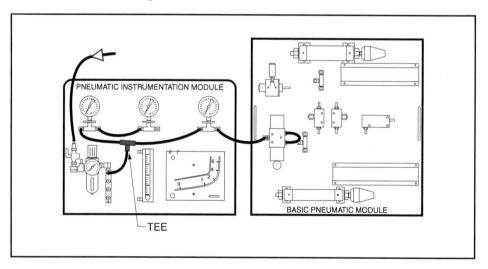

Figure 11. Pictorial of a Circuit for Demonstrating Pascal's Law

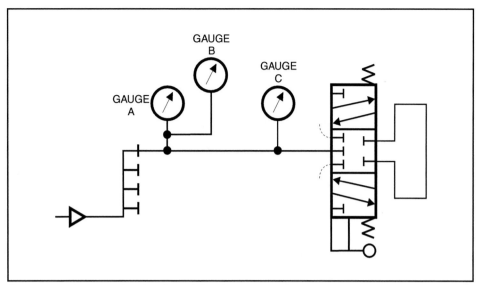

Figure 12. Schematic of a Circuit for Demonstrating Pascal's Law

❑ 3. Perform the following substeps to provide compressed air to the DCV.

    A. Open the shut-off valve.

    B. Turn the regulator adjustment CW until the pressure at the regulator gauge reads 40 psi / 276 kPa.

❑ 4. Record the pressures indicated at Gauges A, B, and C.

    Gauge A _____ (psi / kPa)

    Gauge B _____ (psi / kPa)

    Gauge C _____ (psi / kPa)

You should observe that gauges A, B, and C read the same pressure, 40 psi / 276 kPa (or very close). This is because these gauges are sensing pressure from the same fluid that is confined in the lines. This is Pascal's Law.

NOTE

You may observe that gauge readings differ as much as 5 psi from each other. This is not because the pressure isn't the same, but that the gauges are not set accurately. To set the gauges accurately, a procedure called calibration would be required.

❑ 5. Now shift the DCV and hold it shifted to allow air to flow through the circuit. Observe the new pressure gauge readings.

Gauge A _____ (psi / kPa)

Gauge B _____ (psi / kPa)

Gauge C _____ (psi / kPa)

You should observe that the pressure reading of Gauges A and B are about the same, but Gauge C is different. The reason is that the fluid between Gauges A and C is no longer confined; it is flowing. Since pressure drops as it flows through the tubing, the pressure is lower at Gauge C than gauge A. However, the fluid in the hose connected between Gauges A and B is confined. It is not moving and, therefore, the pressure is the same at both Gauges A and B. This is Pascal's Law.

❑ 6. Release the handle of the DCV.

You should observe that all gauges now read the same as in step 4 because the fluid is contained once again.

❑ 7. Close the shutoff valve and reduce the pressure to minimum by turning the regulator adjustment CCW fully.

❑ 8. Shift the handle of the DCV back and forth to remove all pressure from the circuit.

❑ 9. Set up the circuit shown in figure 13.

This circuit uses a directional control valve to reciprocate a cylinder.

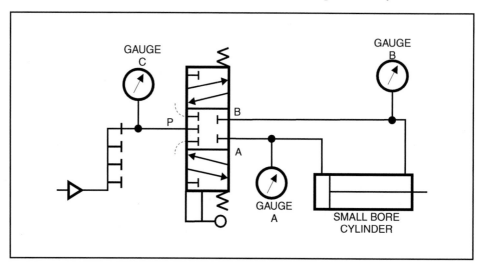

Figure 13. Schematic of a Cylinder Circuit for Demonstrating Pascal's Law

❑ 10. Perform the following substeps to provide compressed air to the DCV.

A. Open the shut-off valve.

B. Turn the regulator adjustment CW until the pressure at the regulator gauge reads 20 psi/138 kPa.

Compressed air is now at Port P of the DCV. Gauge C should read approximately 20 psi/138 kPa since it is measuring pressure in the same confined space as the regulator. Gauges A and B should show 0 psi/0 kPa.

☐11. Now push in on the lever of the DCV to extend the cylinder and observe the pressures at Gauges A and C while the cylinder is extending.

Gauge A _____ (psi / kPa)

Gauge C _____ (psi / kPa)

When the cylinder is extending, the pressure should be low because there is no load on the cylinder.

☐12. When the cylinder is fully extended, continue to hold the lever of the DCV shifted and observe the readings of Gauges A and C.

Gauge A _____ (psi / kPa)

Gauge C _____ (psi / kPa)

Fluid is no longer flowing between Gauges A and C. Therefore, they should be at the same pressure according to Pascal's Law.

☐13. Now pull out the lever of the DCV to retract the cylinder. Observe the pressure at Gauges B and C while the cylinder is retracting.

Gauge B _____ (psi / kPa)

Gauge C _____ (psi / kPa)

You should observe that the pressure is low when the cylinder is retracting.

☐14. When the cylinder is fully retracted, continue to hold the lever of the DCV shifted and observe the readings of Gauges B and C.

Gauge B _____ (psi / kPa)

Gauge C _____ (psi / kPa)

Fluid is no longer flowing between Gauges B and C, so they should be at the same pressure as predicted by Pascal's Law. This shows that full force is available at the actuator when it is stopped.

☐15. Release the lever.

☐16. Repeat steps 11 through 15 to verify your readings.

☐17. Close the shutoff valve and reduce the pressure to minimum by turning the regulator adjustment CCW fully.

☐18. Remove any pressure still in the circuit by shifting the DCV handle back and forth.

One of the most important features of a pneumatic system is its ability to generate a large force output using a small force (pressure) input. This principle is called force multiplication or pneumatic leverage. The principle of force multiplication is based on the pressure/force/area relationship in a fluid system and Pascal's Law. As an example, let's consider the system shown in figure 14.

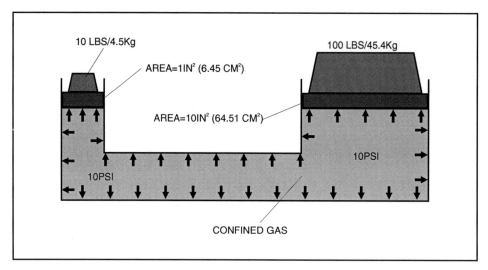

Figure 14. Force Multiplication or Pneumatic Leverage

In this example, an outside force of 10 pounds is applied over a small piston with a 1-square-inch area. This creates 10 psi pressure in the confined fluid. Pascal's Law says this 10 psi is the same throughout the fluid. This means that 10 psi acts against the larger 10-square-inch piston. This 10 psi causes an output force of 100 pounds because of the piston's larger area. So, for the 10-pound input force in this example, we multiplied the force by a factor of 10 to 100 pounds. This is pneumatic leverage.

In an industrial-type pneumatic system, as shown in figure 15, the pressure already in the air compressor's storage tank would be used directly instead of a small piston to create the pressure. But the principle of pneumatic leverage still applies. In this case, it means that a low pressure conducted through small lines could generate a high force output at the cylinder by using a cylinder with a very large area.

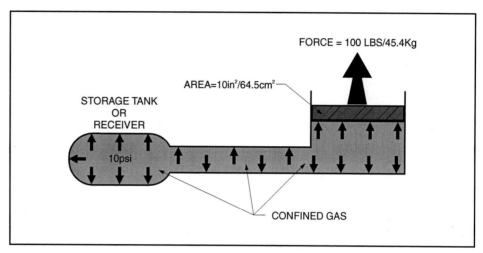

Figure 15. Force Multiplication with Compressed Air

A practical example of force multiplication is the tractor-trailer brake system. Low pressure air is applied across the large area in the brake cylinder to obtain a high output force at the brake drum.

This ability to multiply the force output is an advantage of pneumatics and is one reason why pneumatics is used in many applications.

Unfortunately, pneumatic leverage or force multiplication is not free. Just like the mechanical lever, distance (volume) is sacrificed. In our example of figure 14, to move the 100-pound load (force) 1 inch, the 10-pound input load would need to be moved 10 inches. In figure 15, this would mean that a greater volume of air at 10 psi would be needed as forces are multiplied.

Activity 2. Demonstrate How Distance is Sacrificed to Obtain Force Multiplication

---

Procedure Overview

In this activity, you will connect two cylinders of different sizes together and measure the distance that the larger bore cylinder moves for a six-inch movement of the small bore cylinder.

☐ 1. Before connecting the two cylinders together, use the following substeps to fully retract the large bore cylinder and fully extend the small bore cylinder.

A. Connect hoses to both cylinder ports of each cylinder. This will open both ports to the atmosphere.

B. Grab the large bore cylinder's rod cam and push the cylinder rod to the fully retracted position. With both ends of the cylinder open, the cylinder rod will move easily.

C. Grab the small bore cylinder's rod cam and pull the cylinder rod to the fully extended position.

☐ 2. Connect the cylinders as shown in figure 16.

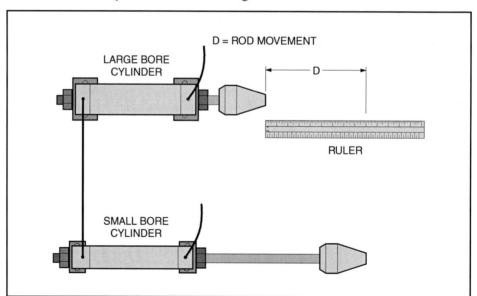

Figure 16. Pictorial of Cylinders Connected Together

❑ 3. Place a ruler next to the large bore cylinder rod, as shown in figure 16, so that its movement can be measured.

❑ 4. Now slowly push in on the rod of the small bore cylinder until it is completely retracted, holding it there about 15 seconds before releasing. The complete stroke of the small bore cylinder is 6 inches.

Measure the distance the large bore cylinder rod has moved as a result.

Rod movement _____ (in / cm)

The large bore cylinder rod should have moved about half the distance of the small bore cylinder rod showing that distance is sacrificed to obtain force multiplication.

1. Pascal's Law states that pressure on a(n) _____ fluid is transmitted undiminished to every portion of a container.

2. Pneumatic actuators may be _____ indefinitely without damage.

3. Using pneumatic leverage, _____ is multiplied.

4. One significance of Pascal's Law is that it makes it possible for pneumatic systems to generate a(n) _____ force with a(n) _____ input pressure to move a load.

5. 75 psi acting across an area of five square inches produces _____ lbs of force.

6. The pressure needed to produce 500 lbs. of force on an eight square inch area is _____ psi.

7. A procedure called _____ is required in order to set gauges accurately.

SEGMENT 3

PRESSURE AND VOLUME

OBJECTIVE 5	DESCRIBE TWO METHODS OF REPRESENTING PRESSURE

Pneumatic pressure can be stated in two ways:
- Absolute pressure
- Gauge pressure

Absolute Pressure

As shown in figure 17, the atmosphere exerts a pressure at sea level that is equal to 14.7 psi or 101 kPa. This is also referred to as 14.7 psia or 14.7 pounds per square inch absolute pressure.

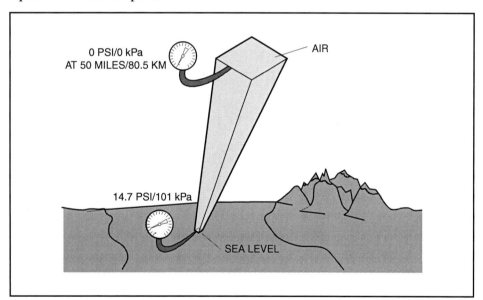

Figure 17. The Pressure of the Atmosphere

If we used an absolute pressure gauge to measure the pressure at a point in space above the atmosphere, the gauge would read 0 psi/0 kPa. This value represents a perfect vacuum because there is no air pressure exerting a force on the pressure gauge. At sea level, this same gauge would read 14.7 psi/101 kPa.

The units you should use to represent absolute pressure are psia or kPa (absolute).

Gauge Pressure

Gauge pressure indicates the amount of pressure above atmospheric pressure. It is the pressure that has been used in the skills and activities contained in these LAPs. Almost all pressure gauges used in pneumatics are designed to indicate gauge pressure. They are adjusted to read 0 psi/0 kPa when exposed to atmospheric pressure at sea level.

When indicating gauge pressure, use psig or just psi. In the S.I. system, the units of kPa are used for both absolute and gauge pressure.

Gauge pressures are easily converted to absolute pressures using the following formula.

GAUGE/ABSOLUTE PRESSURE FORMULA:

$$P_{abs} = P_{gauge} + P_{atm}$$

Where:

P_{abs} = *Absolute Pressure (psia / kPa absolute)*
P_{gauge} = *Gauge Pressure (psig / kPa)*
P_{atm} = *Atmospheric Pressure (psia / kPa absolute)*
(at sea level atmospheric is 14.7 psi / 101 kPa)

NOTE

The exact value of atmospheric pressure shown in the above formula is for sea level. This value will differ according to the elevation.

It is important to understand the difference between gauge and absolute pressure for several reasons:

- Many design calculations require you to convert between absolute and gauge.
- Pressure gauges must be specified as gauge or absolute when they are used.
- The absolute pressure range from 0 to atmospheric is what allows air to be drawn into the compressor.

Procedure Overview

In this procedure, you will develop your skill in converting between gauge and absolute pressure.

❑ 1. Convert the following gauge pressures to absolute pressures.

PRESSURES	
GAUGE (psi/kPa)	ABSOLUTE (psia/kPa absolute)
20/138	/
82/566	/
15.7/108	/
125/863	/

❑ 2. Convert the following absolute pressures to gauge pressures.

PRESSURES	
ABSOLUTE (psia/kPa absolute)	GAUGE (psi/kPa)
35/241.5	/
110/759	/
62.7/433	/
22.3/154	/

As you know, a pneumatic system uses air pressure that is several times greater than atmospheric pressure. This higher air pressure is created by increasing the density of air in a closed container. This is called compressing air, and the machine used to do this in a pneumatic system is called an air compressor.

To understand how this works, you must first know that at sea level a volume of air consists of a large quantity of molecules. These molecules are constantly in motion, causing collisions between themselves as well as with any surfaces exposed to them. When they collide with a rigid surface, they create a pressure.

The amount of pressure depends on the air density. Air density is a measure of the number of molecules contained in a given volume. This fact was shown in the previous objective. At sea level, the air exerts 14.7 psia on all objects. At elevations above sea level, the pressure is less. The air pressure is higher at sea level because the air density is higher. In other words, there are more molecules contained in each cubic meter of air. This larger number of molecules causes more collisions to take place and therefore creates the higher air pressure.

This effect also applies to compressed air systems. The container with more molecules has a higher pressure, as shown in figure 18.

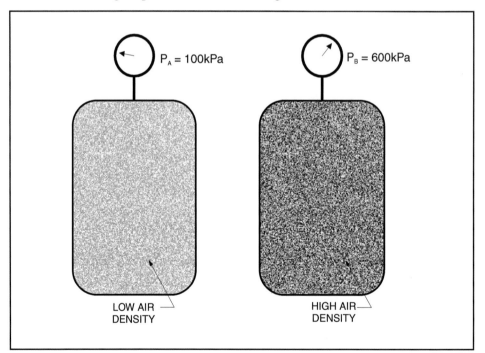

Figure 18. Effect of Air Density on Air Pressure

An air compressor creates pressurized air by reducing the volume of the air. The most basic of air compressors uses one or more pistons, as shown in figure 19, to compress individual volumes of air drawn in from the atmosphere. After each volume of air is compressed, it is pushed into the storage tank.

The details of air compressor operation will be discussed in a later LAP. It is important, however, to understand at this point that an air compressor creates pressure, not flow. This is just the opposite of a hydraulic system where the pump creates flow, not pressure.

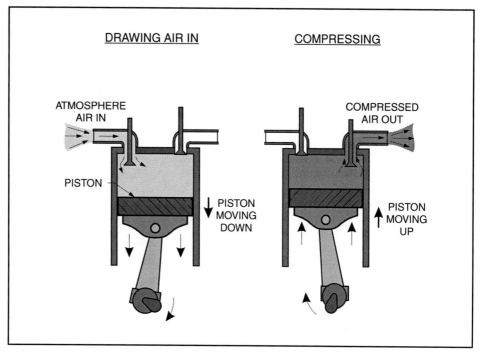

Figure 19. Compressing Action of a Piston-Type Air Compressor

As discussed earlier, an air compressor creates air pressure by reducing its volume. There is a formula used to calculate the exact effect on pressure of a change in volume called Boyle's Law and is stated as follows:

FORMULA: AIR PRESSURE / VOLUME RELATIONSHIP

$$P_1 \times V_1 = P_2 \times V_2$$

Where

$P_1 =$ *Initial Absolute Pressure (psia)*
$V_1 =$ *Initial Volume*
$P_2 =$ *Final Absolute Pressure (psia)*
$V_2 =$ *Final Volume*

Volumes may be stated in cubic inches (in^3), cubic feet (ft^3), cubic centimeters (cm^3), or cubic meters (m^3). Whichever is used, both V_1 and V_2 must be in the same terms.

Boyle's Law shows that if the volume of air in the container, shown in figure 20, is reduced by one half, the pressure will double. Or, stated in another way, volume is inversely proportional to pressure.

Boyle's Law is valid for constant temperature conditions only. Temperature changes will affect pressure and volume. A later LAP will discuss the relationship between pressure, volume, and temperature.

Boyle's Law is very important because it allows the calculation of the sizes of various pneumatic components. As an example, Boyle's Law can be used to determine how large a storage tank needs to be for an air compressor. If a tank is too small, the air compressor will run constantly and burn up. Most air compressors must turn off for a certain period of time to allow them to cool.

Procedure Overview

In this procedure, you will use Boyle's Law to calculate pressures and volumes for a number of air volumes. In steps 1 and 2, we will lead you through two examples, then you will do it yourself.

☐ 1. Determine the final air pressure, $P2$, in the container given the following information:

A volume of air is reduced in size from 20 ft3 to 10 ft3, as shown in figure 20.

The given information is as follows:

$P_1 = 0\ psig\ (14.7\ psia)$

$V_1 = 20\ ft^3$

$V_2 = 10\ ft^3$

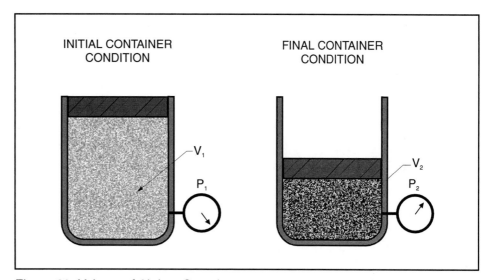

Figure 20. Volume of Air in a Container

The solution for P_2 is as follows:

$P_1 \times V_1 = P_2 \times V_2$

$(14.7 \; psia) \times (20 \; ft^3) = (P_2) \times (10 \; ft^3)$

$P_2 = 14.7 \times 20 \div 10$

$P_2 = 29.4 \; psia$

If you read this pressure from a standard pressure gauge, you would need to convert this pressure to psig as follows:

$P_2 = 29.4 \; psia - 14.7 \; psia = 14.7 \; psig$

❑ 2. Determine the final air pressure, P_2, in a container given the following information.

A container of air is reduced in size from 2 m³ to 1 m³, as shown in figure 20.

Given:

$P_1 = Atmospheric \; pressure, \; or \; 101 \; kPa \; absolute$

$V_1 = 2 \; meter^3$

$V_2 = 1 \; meter^3$

$P_2 = $ _____ (kPa absolute)

The solution for P_2 is as follows:

$(101 \; kPa)(2 \; m^3) = (P_2)(1 \; m^3)$

$P_2 = 202 \; kPa \; absolute$

If you read this pressure from a standard pressure gauge, you will need to convert this pressure to gauge as follows:

$P_2 = 202 \; kPa \; absolute - 101 \; kPa = 101 \; kPa \; gauge$

❑ 3. Calculate the final pressures (P_2) in absolute and gauge terms for the following conditions.

A. $P_1 = 62$ psia

$V_1 = 100$ ft³

$V_2 = 10$ ft³

$P_2 = $ _____ (psia), _____ (psig)

B. $P_1 = 0$ psig

$V_1 = 25$ in³

$V_2 = 1$ in³

$P_2 = $ _____ (psia), _____ (psig)

❑ 4. Calculate the final volumes, V_2, for the following conditions.

A. $P_1 = 25$ kPa

$P_2 = 85$ kPa

$V_1 = 5$ m^3

$V_2 = $ _____ (m^3)

B. $P_1 = 10$ psig

$P_2 = 100$ psig

$V_1 = 20$ ft^3

$V_2 = $ _____ (ft^3)

❑ 5. Determine the size of a storage tank given the following information.

You have just decided to start your own dive shop and you need to buy a large storage tank to hold compressed air to supply air to your customers for their breathing air tanks.

The divers' tanks need 3000 psig / 20,700 kPa of air stored in them. The tank size is 4.0 cubic feet / 0.5 m^3. You will recharge the large tank one time per day and expect 75 divers to use your service each day.

Assume that the storage tank pressure will be 5000 psig / 34,500 kPa.

Find:

Storage Tank Size _____ (ft^3 / m^3)

Activity 3. Verification of Boyle's Law

Procedure Overview

In this procedure, you will verify Boyle's Law by showing how a change in air volume changes pressure. This will be done by compressing air in a cylinder and monitoring pressure.

☐ 1. Perform the following substeps to fully extend the small bore cylinder.

    A. Connect hoses to both cylinder ports. This will open both quick-connects to the atmosphere.

    B. Grab the cylinder rod cam and force the cylinder rod to the fully extended position.

       With both ends of the cylinder open, the cylinder rod will move easily.

☐ 2. Connect the cap end of the cylinder to the pressure gauge, as shown in figure 21.

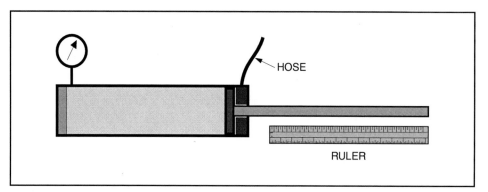

Figure 21. Pictorial of Circuit to Verify Boyle's Law

❑ 3. Set a ruler next to the cylinder rod so its movement can be measured.

❑ 4. Push in the rod of the cylinder to each of the following positions. You will observe that the air pressure in the cylinder rises as you do this. Record the pressure gauge reading for each position listed in the chart. Then convert this pressure to absolute pressure.

ROD POSITION	ACTUAL PRESSURE	
(in/cm)	GAUGE (psi/kPa)	ABSOLUTE (psia/kPa)
6/15.2 (fully extended)	/	/
5/12.7	/	/
4/10.2	/	/
3/7.6	/	/
2/5.1	/	/
1/2.5	/	/

❑ 5. Allow the cylinder to extend.

❑ 6. Now, calculate the theoretical pressure that would be generated by each of the cylinder positions. Use Boyle's Law to do this.

The initial volume, V_1, in the cylinder is found by multiplying the stroke of the cylinder by the area of the piston. Use the initial pressure, (P_1) of 14.7 psi / 101 kPa.

$V_1 =$ _____ (in^3/cm^3)

ROD POSITION	VOLUME, V2	THEORETICAL ABSOLUTE PRESSURE, P_2
(in/cm)	(in^3/cm^3)	(psia/kPa)
6/15.2 (fully extended)	/	/
5/12.7	/	/
4/10.2	/	/
3/7.6	/	/
2/5.1	/	/
1/2.5	/	/

❑ 7. Compare your theoretical calculations to the actual pressure values. They should be reasonably close.

Also, notice the pressure at a rod position of 3 in / 7.6 cm. The pressure at that point should be about twice the pressure (30 psia / 202 kPa absolute) as it is when the rod pointer is at 6 in / 15.2 cm. This is because the volume is reduced by half.

1.   The absolute pressure at sea level is _____ psi / _____ kPa.

2.   To convert gauge pressures to absolute, add _____ pressure to the gauge pressure.

3.   _____ pressures are used in the formula defining Boyle's Law.

4.   _____ pressure indicates the amount of pressure above atmospheric pressure.

5.   Boyle's Law states that pressure is _____ proportional to volume.

6.   4 ft^3 of atmospheric air compressed to 1 ft^3 will be at _____ psig.

7.   The machine used to compress air is called a(n) _____ _____.

SEGMENT 4

AIR FLOW AND RESISTANCE

OBJECTIVE 8	EXPLAIN HOW A PNEUMATIC SYSTEM CREATES AIR FLOW

The two previous Objectives explained that the density of air molecules determines pressure; the greater the density, the greater the pressure. Another characteristic of air is that a difference in pressure causes air flow to occur. Air flows from areas of high pressure to areas of low pressure until the pressure is the same throughout.

This concept is shown in figure 22 where two containers at different pressures are connected together. When the valve is opened, flow occurs from the container with the higher pressure to the container with the lower pressure.

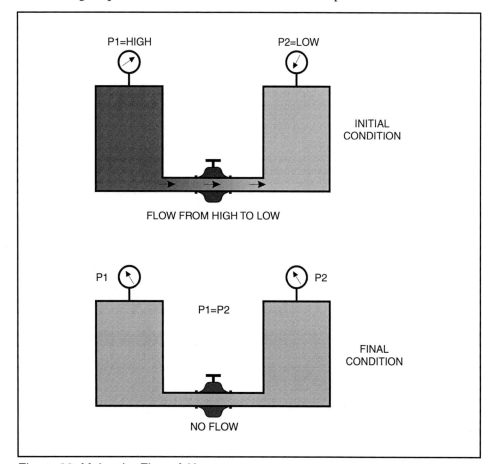

Figure 22. Molecular Flow of Air

The rate at which the air will flow from one container to another depends on the difference in pressure between the two containers and the amount of resistance in the passage. Air flows faster with higher pressure differentials and lower resistances.

If the passage between two air volumes at different pressures is totally unrestricted and the pressure differential is high enough, the air will flow from the high pressure volume to the low pressure volume at a very high speed. In fact, this speed is the speed of sound (1100 ft/sec or 335 m/sec). This is why pneumatic systems are known for being able to generate high speed actuator movement.

OBJECTIVE 9	DESCRIBE TWO TYPES OF RESISTANCE IN A PNEUMATIC SYSTEM

Unfortunately, air flow in a pneumatic system is not unrestricted. There are two resistances to deal with:

- Loads at the actuator
- Air friction

As the resistance of either the load or air friction increases, the flow rate decreases.

Loads at the Actuator

The loads at the actuator, while it is extending or retracting include the load to be moved, mechanical friction of the actuator, and back pressure. Figure 23 shows an example of this concept using a cylinder.

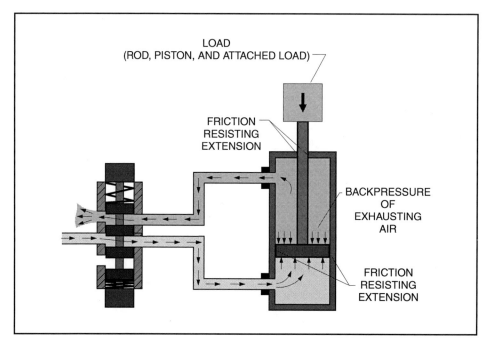

Figure 23. Loads at the Cylinder During Extension

Air Friction

When air flows through the components in a system, it moves against the internal surfaces of the components. No matter how smooth or short the surfaces, there is always some resistance to the air flow caused by the friction between the moving air and the internal surfaces. This resistance causes the air upstream of each component to have a higher pressure than the air downstream in order to push the air through the component. An example of this is shown in figure 24.

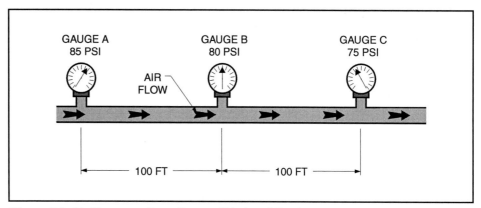

Figure 24. Air Pressure Drop Due to Frictional Resistance in a Pipe

All components through which air flows cause a frictional drop in pressure. These include tubing, hose, fittings, valves, and actuators. The amount of resistance drop depends on the air flow rate and the characteristics of the component such as the size, shape, and roughness of the inside surfaces. If the inside of the component is very large and has smooth surfaces, the resistance will be low.

EXPLAIN HOW DELTA P DESCRIBES PNEUMATIC RESISTANCE AND EXPLAIN ITS IMPORTANCE

The term delta P (ΔP) is often used to describe resistance in a pneumatic system or across the component. Delta P is the difference in pressure between one point in a system and another point in the system. For example, in figure 25, the ΔP between gauge A (motor inlet) and gauge B (motor outlet) is 345 kPa. This is the difference between the pressure at gauges A and B (380 - 35 = 345 kPa).

The ΔP can be caused by either load resistance or frictional resistance. The ΔP for the motor shown in figure 25 is load resistance. The ΔP between the regulator and motor is caused by frictional resistance in the lines and fittings.

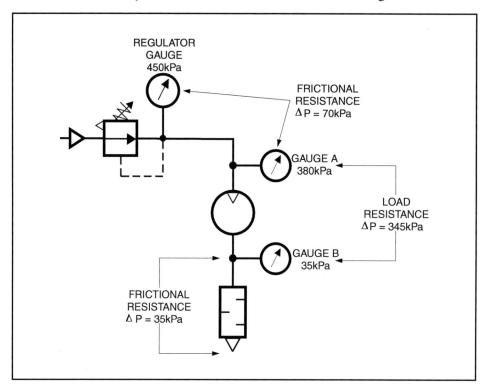

Figure 25. Delta Ps in a Pneumatic Circuit

The ΔP is used to describe resistance because the pressure downstream of the component may not be zero. The ΔP allows you to describe the resistance across the component no matter what the downstream pressure is.

Notice that frictional ΔP decreases the amount of pressure available to power actuators. Too much frictional resistance is not only a waste of power but causes actuators to slow, unless supply pressure is increased. Therefore, it is important in circuit design to be aware of the ΔP of each component so frictional resistances can be kept to a minimum.

Connectors and fittings, especially quick-connect fittings, have high frictional resistances. Unless necessary, avoid using quick-connect fittings.

Procedure Overview

In this procedure, you will demonstrate that as air flows through the components of a circuit, pressure drops occur. Tubing with quick-connects, tees, and a DCV will be used in the circuit to show this.

❑ 1. Connect the circuit shown in figure 26.

When the DCV is shifted in this circuit, air will flow from the supply through the DCV, out one of the DCV cylinder ports, back into the other cylinder port, and back through the DCV to exhaust. The gauges will be used to measure pressure drops through segments of the circuit.

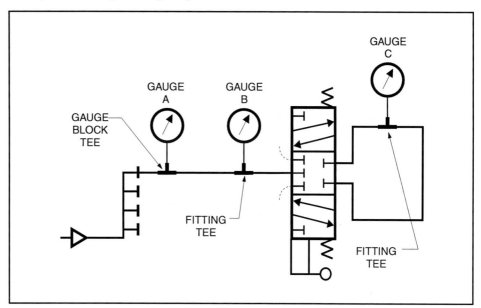

Figure 26. Schematic to Demonstrate Pressure Drop in a Flowing Circuit

❑ 2. Open the shutoff valve.

❑ 3. Turn the regulator adjustment knob CW until the pressure at Gauge A reads 30 psi / 207 kPa.

❑ 4. Now push in on the handle of the DCV and hold it shifted.

This will open the flow paths of the DCV and allow flow from the supply to the exhaust (atmosphere).

❑ 5. Record the pressures of each gauge in the chart next to the initial supply pressure of 30 psi / 207 kPa.

INITIAL SUPPLY PRESSURE (psi/kPa)	GAUGE A (psi/kPa)	GAUGE B (psi/kPa)	GAUGE C (psi/kPa)
30/207	/	/	/
40/276	/	/	/

You should observe that gauge A reads the highest with gauge B next and gauge C the lowest. These pressures show there is a pressure drop across each set of components.

❑ 6. Release the DCV handle to stop flow in the circuit.

❑ 7. Turn the regulator adjustment knob CW until the pressure at Gauge A reads 40 psi/276 kPa and repeat steps 4-6.

❑ 8. From the pressures recorded in the table of step 5, calculate the pressure drops for each segment of the circuit listed in the chart.

CIRCUIT SEGMENT	PRESSURE DROP (ΔP)	
	30 psi/207kPa	40 psi/276 kPa
Gauge A-B	/	/
Gauge B-C	/	/

The pressure drop between gauges A and B is caused by the resistance of the tube, 1/2 fitting tee, 1/2 gauge block tee, and two quick-connect fittings. The pressure drop between Gauges B and C is caused by the resistance across one path of the DCV, a fitting tee, two hoses, and four quick-connects.

You should observe that each pressure and pressure drop increases as the supply pressure is increased from 30 psi to 40 psi. This is because flow rate increases as supply pressure increases.

❑ 9. Turn the regulator adjustment CCW to reduce pressure to a minimum.

❑ 10. Close the shutoff valve.

❑ 11. Move the lever of the DCV back and forth to remove any pressure still in the circuit.

❑ 12. Calculate the total ΔP for this circuit between Gauges A, B, and C and list below.

ΔP total at 30 psi/207 kPa =(psi/kPa)

ΔP total at 40 psi/276 kPa =(psi/kPa)

❏13. Now remove Gauge B, Gauge B fitting tee, and the tubing between Gauge B fitting tee and the DCV from the circuit and connect the tubing from gauge block A to the DCV P-Port.

With these components removed, you will be able to see how much resistance is in a piece of tubing, a tee, and two quick-connects.

❏14. Open the shutoff valve and adjust the regulator to where 30 psi/207 kPa is at Gauge A.

❏15. Repeat step 4 and record in the chart below for supply pressure settings of 30 psi/207 kPa and 40 psi/276 kpa.

SUPPLY PRESSURE	GAUGE A (psi/kPa)	GAUGE B (psi/kPa)	DP A-C (psi/kPa)
30 psi/207 kPa	/	/	/
40 psi/276 kPa	/	/	/

❏16. Calculate the ΔP at each supply pressure and place in the chart of step 15.

❏17. Now take the ΔPs obtained in step 16 and subtract those obtained in step 12. Record below.

ΔP at 30 psi/207 kPa supply = _____ (psi/kPa)

ΔP at 40 psi/276 kPa supply = _____ (psi/kPa)

These DPs show how much resistance is in a piece of tube, tee, and two quick-connects. Assuring little resistance from the tubing and tee, this should show that quick-connects have a relatively high resistance.

❏18. Turn the regulator adjustment CCW to reduce pressure to minimum.

❏19. Close the shutoff valve.

❏20. Move the lever of the DCV back and forth to remove any pressure still in the circuit.

In hydraulics, the speed of an actuator depends on the amount of volume flow from the pump. If the pump provides more flow, the actuator will move faster.

In pneumatics, the speed of the actuator is not affected at all by the pump flow (In this case, the pump is the air compressor), because the air compressor's flow goes into a storage tank to be used as needed by the system.

Instead, pneumatic actuator speed depends on the amount of pressure at the regulator that is in excess of that needed to overcome the resistances described in Objective 9. As this excess pressure increases, so does actuator speed.

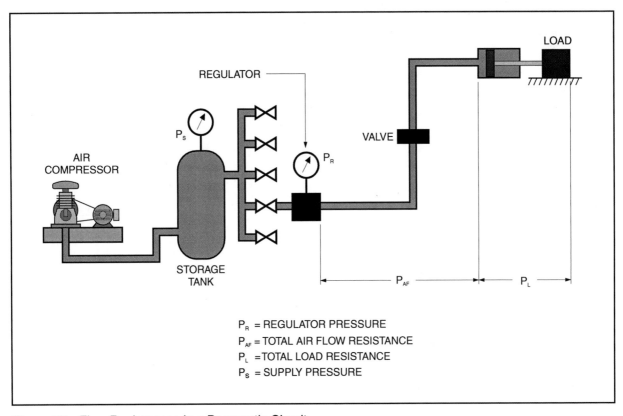

P_R = REGULATOR PRESSURE
P_{AF} = TOTAL AIR FLOW RESISTANCE
P_L = TOTAL LOAD RESISTANCE
P_S = SUPPLY PRESSURE

Figure 27.   Flow Resistances in a Pneumatic Circuit

From figure 27, the excess pressure that causes flow can be determined by using the following formula:

FORMULA: EXCESS PRESSURE

$$P_x = P_R - P_{AF} - P_L$$

Where:

P_x = *Excess Pressure*
P_R = *Regulator Pressure*
P_{AF} = *Total Air Flow Resistance*
P_L = *Total Load Resistance*

This means that the speed of a pneumatic actuator can be increased by anything that causes Px to be higher. This includes increasing the regulator pressure, decreasing the load, or decreasing the air resistance in the circuit.

There is a limit, however, to how fast air will move. When air speed at any point in the circuit reaches the speed of sound, an increase in Px will no longer have an effect on actuator speed.

Activity 4. Effect of Pressure on Pneumatic Actuator Speed

Procedure Overview

In this procedure, you will connect a double-acting cylinder in a reciprocating circuit and measure the times to extend at various supply pressures.

❑ 1. Before you connect your cylinder circuit, perform the following substeps.

    A. Close the shutoff valve.

    B. Adjust the regulator to its minimum pressure setting.

    C. Connect the compressed air supply source to the supply connection located on the pneumatic instrumentation module.

❑ 2. Connect the small double-acting cylinder in the pneumatic circuit shown in figure 28.

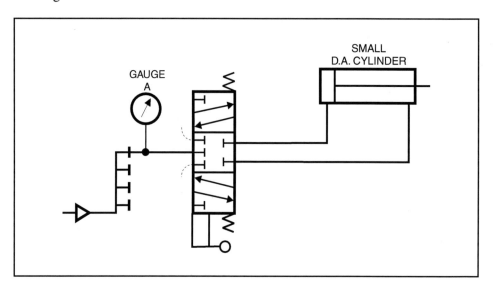

Figure 28. Schematic of a Cylinder Reciprocation Circuit

❑ 3. Open the shutoff valve.

❑ 4. Slowly turn the regulator adjustment knob CW until the pressure at Gauge A reads 5 psi / 34.5 kPa.

Notice that the pressure gauge is graduated in 2 psi/13.8 kPa increments and starts at 4 psi/27.6 kPa. This indicates that the gauge is inaccurate below 4 psi/27.6 kPa. It is normal for a gauge to be inaccurate near 0 psi/0 kPa.

❑ 5. Try to extend and retract the cylinder by shifting the handle of the DCV. As you do this, the pressure will probably drop off and the cylinder will stop in mid-stroke. At this low pressure, the regulator is difficult to set because of friction.

❑ 6. Release the handle of the DCV and readjust the regulator so Gauge A again reads 5 psi / 34.5 kPa.

❑ 7. Repeat steps 5 and 6 until the pressure at Gauge A will remain at 5 psi / 34.5 kPa when the DCV is blocking flow.

❑ 8. Using the DCV, extend and retract the cylinder while timing the extension time with a stopwatch. Record these times in the following chart.

GAUGE A PRESSURE (psi/kPa)	EXTENSION TIME (SEC)			
	Trial 1	Trial 2	Trial 3	Average
5/34.5				
6/41.4				
8/55.2				
10/69				

You should observe that even at this low pressure, the cylinder extends rapidly. That is why pneumatics is used in high-speed applications.

❑ 9. Repeat step 8 for the other pressures shown in the chart.

You should observe that as pressure increases, the time to extend decreases. This shows that the higher the pressure the faster the speed of the actuator.

❑10. With the cylinder fully retracted, turn the regulator adjustment CCW to reduce pressure to a minimum.

❑11. Close the shutoff valve.

❑12. Move the lever of the DCV back and forth to remove any pressure still in the circuit.

1. Air will flow when there is a(n) _____ _____.

2. Delta P is the _____ in pressure between two points in a pneumatic system.

3. Increasing the air pressure to an actuator as it is moving a load will increase the _____.

4. The maximum speed of air flow occurs at the speed of _____.

5. DP allows you to describe the resistance of a component regardless of the _____ pressure.